Mike Cornick

BLUE
PIANO DUETS

www.universaledition.com

vienna · london · new york

UE 21006

ISMN M-008-06197-4
UPC 8-03452-05028-5
ISBN 978-3-7024-3296-6

PREFACE

With the exception of *Out Of The Blue*, these duets have been written using the swing quaver symbol:

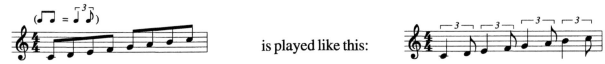

The use of this rhythmic convention, which instructs players to treat all quaver movement (including quaver rests and tied quavers) with a "swing" feel, avoids much of the complication in notating jazz and allows the player to apply the degree of "swing" as a matter of interpretation.

Players who are unused to jazz may well benefit from practising a few scales and phrases beforehand, so giving themselves the opportunity of becoming familiar with swinging the quavers:

With the swing quaver symbol present, the C-major scale which appears like this:

   is played like this:

Taking a further example, the opening *Primo* bars of *Temporary Diversion,* although notated like this:

will be played like this:

VORWORT

Mit Ausnahme von *Out Of The Blue* wurden bei den vorliegenden Kompositionen Swing-Achtel verwendet:

Durch diese rhythmische Konvention, bei welcher der Spieler dazu angehalten ist, sämtliche Achtel (auch Achtelpausen und gebundene Achtel) „swingend" zu spielen, können die Schwierigkeiten bei der Notation von Jazz großteils umgangen werden. Wieviel Swing eingebracht wird, ist eine Frage der Interpretation und liegt im Ermessen des Pianisten.

Für Spieler, die mit Jazz nicht vertraut sind, ist es ratsam, zuvor einige isolierte Phrasen und Abschnitte zu üben und sich so an die mit Swing zu spielenden Achtel zu gewöhnen:

Bei Verwendung der Swing-Achtel wird die C-Dur Tonleiter, die wie folgt erscheint:

   folgendermaßen gespielt:

Ein weiteres Beispiel zeigt, dass die Anfangstakte für *Primo* aus *Temporary Diversion,* obwohl sie wie folgt notiert sind:

folgendermaßen gespielt werden:

CONTENTS

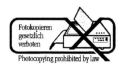

Late Night Call

MIKE CORNICK

Universal Edition UE 21006

Late Night Call

MIKE CORNICK

4

quasi walking bass

Out Of The Blue

MIKE CORNICK

Out Of The Blue

Slowly and pensively ($\quarternote$ = 95)
(in even quavers)

MIKE CORNICK

Temporary Diversion

MIKE CORNICK

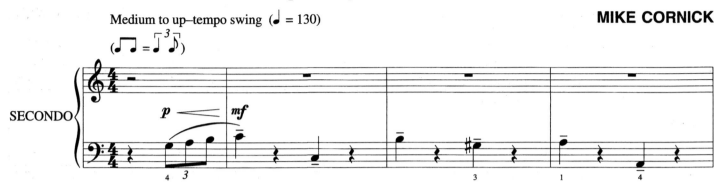

Temporary Diversion

Medium to up–tempo swing (♩ = 130)

MIKE CORNICK

PRIMO

UE 21006

Inconsequential Blues

MIKE CORNICK

Inconsequential Blues

MIKE CORNICK

Piano Dance

Up–tempo swing (♩ = 135)

MIKE CORNICK

Piano Dance

MIKE CORNICK

Universal Edition

Further titles by Mike Cornick

Solo

Boogie Piano Book	(3–4)*	UE 16 592
Barrel House Piano	(5–6)	UE 17 375
Dixieland Piano	(4–6)	UE 21 025
Piano Ragtime	(4–5)	UE 30 413
Easy Blue Piano	(2–3)	UE 21 260
Blue Piano	(4–6)	UE 19 762
Latin Piano	(3–6)	UE 17 365
Take Another 10 – Piano	(3–6)	UE 21 171
Easy Bar Piano – Rock & Pop (with CD), Germ.	(2–5)	UE 31 843
Easy Bar Piano – Rock & Pop (with CD), Eng.	(2–5)	UE 31 843 E
Easy Jazzy Piano 1	(2–5)	UE 16 550
Easy Jazzy Piano 2	(3–5)	UE 16 590
Jazz After Hours	(4–6)	UE 21 099
The Christmas Keyboard Songbook	(1–2)	UE 21 076
On The Right Track 1 (with CD)	(2–3)	UE 21 124
On The Right Track 2 (with CD)	(3–4)	UE 21 125
On The Right Track 3 (with CD)	(5–6)	UE 21 147
On The Right Track 4 (with CD)	(6–8)	UE 21 163
20 Piano Studies	(4–5)	UE 21 233
30 Easy Piano Studies	(1–3)	UE 21 298
Blue Baroque	(3-6+)	UE 21 315

Tutors

Jazz Improvisation for Piano & Keyboard (with CD)	(2–4)	UE 14 050
Start Pianojazz	(1–3)	UE 17 361
Pianojazz 1	(2–3)	UE 17 391
Pianojazz 2	(3–4)	UE 17 392
Pianojazz 3	(5–6)	UE 17 393
Skillbuilder 1	(2–3)	UE 21 077
Skillbuilder 2	(3–4)	UE 21 078
Skillbuilder 3	(5–6)	UE 21 079

4 Hands (6 Hands)

Tea for Two	(4–5)	UE 21 299
Charleston for Two	(4–5)	UE 21 368
Blue Piano Duets	(6)	UE 21 006
Boogie Piano Duets	(4–5)	UE 18 796
Easy Jazzy Duets	(2–4)	UE 16 577
Jazzy Duets Piano 1	(3–4)	UE 19 756
Jazzy Duets Piano 2	(3–5)	UE 16 536
Latin Piano Duets	(4–6)	UE 21 007
Piano Ragtime Duets	(4–5)	UE 16 591
3 Pieces For 6 Hands at 1 Piano	(6–7)	UE 21 123
4 Pieces For 6 Hands at 1 Piano	(2–4)	UE 21 300

* Approximate Gradings 1–8 = Easy to Advanced

www.universaledition.com
vienna · london · new york

655/XII 2006